HOUGHTON MIFFLIN

Georgia
Science

🐦 HOUGHTON MIFFLIN

Printed in the U.S.A.
ISBN 13: 978-0-547-12510-7
ISBN 10: 0-547-12510-0

3 4 5 6 7 8 9 0877 15 14 13 12 11 10 09

Contents

What Do You Know?

Talk with a partner. List different types of weather. (Circle) the words that tell about weather where you live.

_____

_____

_____

Weather Patterns

Contents

What Do You Want to Know?
What do you wonder about weather?

_____

_____

_____

_____

_____

_____

VOCABULARY

condenses Changes from water vapor to drops of water. (*verb*)

evaporates Changes to a gas. The Sun warms water, and water evaporates. (*verb*)

precipitation Water that falls from clouds. (*noun*)

water cycle Water moving from Earth to the air and back again. (*noun*)

water vapor Water as a gas. You cannot see water vapor. (*noun*)

1 How Does Weather Change?

Weather changes over time.
These changes happen again and again in the same order, or pattern.
Weather can change from day to day.
Weather can also change during the day.

S2E3a. Recognize effects that occur in a specific area caused by weather, plants, animals, and/or people.

Daily Weather Patterns

The Sun warms the air during the day.
This makes the afternoon air warmer than the morning air.
The air cools at night.
The temperature tells how warm or cool the air is.
Temperature is measured with a thermometer.

thermometer

1. Circle the temperature on the thermometer. Record the temperature here.

_____

2. Tell how you would feel if the temperature were 95°.

_____

_____

_____

I Wonder . . . I know that weather can change during the day. What different kinds of weather might happen today?

_____

_____

_____

_____

_____

_____

_____

Sudden Changes

Sometimes weather can change very fast.
The Sun might be out in the morning.
Then clouds move in.
It rains in the afternoon.

a storm over Tampa, Florida

Meteorologists are scientists who study the weather.
They use tools to tell what kind of weather is coming.
They use radar to keep track of weather changes.

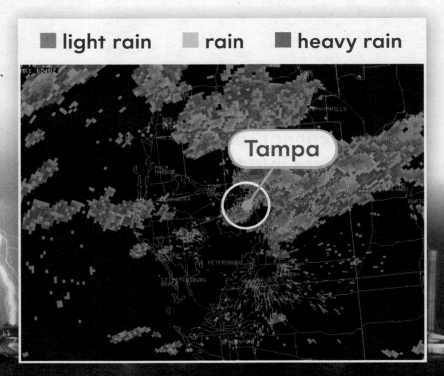

light rain   rain   heavy rain

Tampa

The radar shows the storm over Tampa, Florida.

3. What does a meteorologist do?

_____

Circle the correct answer.

4. In the radar map, what does the color green stand for?

(A) rain

(B) light rain

(C) heavy rain

S2E3a

5. Circle a place on the map where there is heavy rain.

7

6. Put an X on the picture where water is evaporating.

7. What happens when a puddle is warmed by the Sun?

_____

The Water Cycle

The Sun warms water.
This causes water to change and move.
Water moving from Earth to the air and back again is called the **water cycle**.

2 Water as a gas is called water vapor. You cannot see it. It mixes into the air.

1 The Sun warms the water. The water evaporates, or changes to a gas.

3 Air with water vapor rises and cools.
Water vapor **condenses**, or changes to drops of water.
These drops of water make clouds.

4 The drops get bigger and heavier.
The drops fall to the ground.
The drops can be rain, snow, sleet, or hail.

5 Rain and melted snow collect in rivers, lakes, and oceans.
The water cycle begins again.

8. Fill in the blanks. Tell how clouds form.

a. Air with water vapor _____ and _____ .

b. Water vapor _____, or changes to drops of water.

c. The water drops _____ .

9. What is precipitation?

_____

_____

_____

10. Look at the picture on this page.
What kind of precipitation is shown?

_____

Precipitation

Precipitation is water that falls from clouds.

Rain and snow are kinds of precipitation.

Rain falls when the air is warm.

Snow falls when the air is cold.

Sleet and hail are kinds of precipitation, too.
Sleet is falling snow that melts and freezes again.
Hail is falling rain that freezes into balls of ice.

hail

11. Fill in the blanks. Tell how sleet forms.

a. _____ falls through the air.

b. The falling snow _____.

c. The melted snow _____.

12. Look at the picture on this page. How do you know that the wind is blowing?

_____

_____

_____

13. Look at the picture on page 13. How do you know that the wind has been blowing?

_____

_____

_____

Wind

Wind is moving air.
Wind can be gentle.
Wind can be strong.

strong winds

Strong winds may blow during storms.
Strong winds can blow falling rain.
Strong winds can blow snow.
Wind can blow snow into drifts.

snow in drifts

Main Idea

What are two different kinds of precipitation?

Summary   Weather changes in patterns over time.
How might the weather change in one day?

_____

_____

_____

▶ **Main Idea**   What are two different kinds of precipitation?

Main Idea

Kinds of Precipitation

Detail

_____

_____

Detail

_____

_____

13

VOCABULARY

season A time of year. *(noun)*

VOCABULARY ACTIVITY

Use Words

season

List four words on page 14 that help you understand the word **season**.

_____

GPS **S2E2c.** Relate the length of day and night to the change in seasons (for example: Days are longer than the night in the summer.).

2 What Is the Pattern of the Seasons?

A **season** is a time of year.
The four seasons are winter, spring, summer, and fall.
They are always in this order.
Each season has its own weather pattern.
Air temperatures are different in each season.

Bismarck, North Dakota

Oklahoma City, Oklahoma

Winter is the coolest season.
In spring, temperatures slowly rise.
Summer is the warmest season.
In fall, temperatures slowly fall.
Different places have different
weather patterns.
Winter is very cold in some places.
Winter is just a littler cooler than
summer in other places.

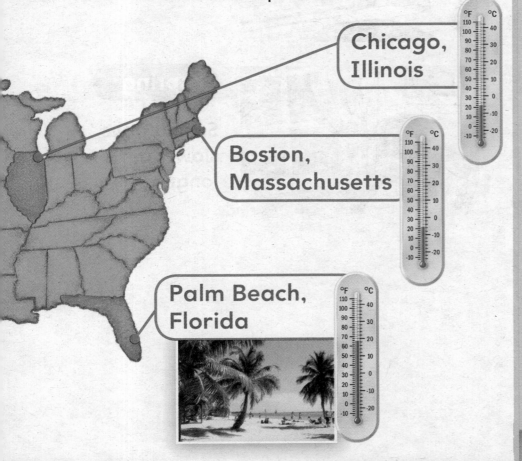

Chicago, Illinois

Boston, Massachusetts

Palm Beach, Florida

1. Look at the thermometers on pages 14 and 15. List the temperature for each of the cities.

_____

_____

_____

_____

2. Tell what winter is like where you live.

_____

_____

_____

_____

3. All the pictures show the same time of day. Tell how the Sun is different in the pictures.

Winter:

_____

_____

Spring:

_____

_____

Summer:

_____

_____

Fall:

_____

_____

Daylight Patterns

The Sun shines during the day. The number of daylight hours is different in each season.

winter

Winter days are the shortest.

spring

Spring days slowly get longer.

Summer has the most hours of daylight.
The Sun warms the land and the water for a longer time.
Summer has the warmest weather.

summer

Summer days are the longest.

fall

Fall days slowly get shorter.

Sequence

How does the number of daylight hours change as the seasons change?

Summary Each season has its own weather pattern. Which season is warmest and has the longest daylight hours?

_____

▶ **Sequence** How does the number of daylight hours change as the seasons change?

Winter
Daytime is shortest.

↓

Spring
_____

↓

Summer
Daytime is longest.

↓

Fall
Daytime slowly gets shorter.

VOCABULARY

hibernate To go into a deep sleep. *(verb)*

migrate To move to warmer places in fall. *(verb)*

VOCABULARY ACTIVITY

Use Syllables

hibernate

Break the word into syllables.

Say each syllable aloud.

Clap once for each syllable.

How many syllables are in the word **hibernate**?

  S2L1b. Relate seasonal changes to observations of how a tree changes throughout a school year.

3 How Do Living Things Change With the Seasons?

Changes in the seasons cause plants and animals to change.

As air warms or cools, living things change.

As the number of daylight hours changes, living things change.

Changes with the Seasons

Season	spring	summer
How a Tree Changes		

Plants and the Seasons

Plants change with the seasons.
In spring, many plants flower.
In summer, fruit grows.
In fall, leaves on some plants change color.
In winter, plants stop growing.

fall	winter

I. Draw what a tree would look like in spring.

CRCT Prep

Circle the correct answer.

2. The tree stops growing in the winter because the days are

(A) longer.

(B) shorter.

(C) warmer.

S2L1b

19

3. What does the deer look like in the spring?

_____

Animals and the Seasons

Animals change with the seasons. Some animals change how they look.

In spring, a male deer's antlers begin to grow.

Some animals grow thicker fur in the fall and winter.
Their fur may change color, too.

In fall, the deer's antlers are fully grown.
The deer's fur gets thicker.

4. Look at the deer in spring and fall. (Circle) what changed about the deer.

5. What is different about the deer's fur in fall?

_____

_____

_____

_____

_____

I Wonder . . . I know that animals change when the seasons change. Why do some animals store food and others hibernate?

_____

_____

_____

_____

Most animals change what they do as the seasons change.
Some animals save food in the fall to eat in the winter.
Other animals **hibernate**, or go into a deep sleep, in winter.
In spring, they wake up.
Then they find food and have their young.

A ground squirrel hibernates in winter.

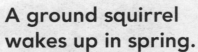

A ground squirrel wakes up in spring.

Some animals **migrate**, or move to warmer places, in fall.
These animals can find food in the warm places.

Some butterflies migrate in fall.

Look at the picture below to answer numbers 6 and 7.

6. Circle the migrating animals.

7. Put an X on the hibernating animal.

Summary Changes in the seasons cause plants and animals to change. What changes have you observed in fall?

_____

_____

_____

 Compare and Contrast

Tell how a plant is different in two seasons.

Compare	Contrast
In spring, plants flower.	_____
	_____
	_____
	_____
	_____

24

Dressing for the Seasons

People change with the seasons. They change what they do. They change what they wear.

A hat helps keep in body heat.

Layers of clothes keep heat near your body.

Socks and shoes keep your feet warm and dry.

Compare and Contrast

Tell how a plant is different in two seasons.

condenses Changes from water vapor to drops of water.

evaporates Changes to a gas. The Sun warms water, and water evaporates.

hibernate To go into a deep sleep.

migrate To move to warmer places in fall.

(Circle) the words that have three syllables.

Write one sentence with two science words.

_____

_____

_____

Visit www.eduplace.com/gascp to play word games and puzzles.

Choose two science words.

Write each word three times.

_____   _____

_____   _____

_____   _____

precipitation Water that falls from clouds.

season A time of year.

water cycle Water moving from Earth to the air and back again.

water vapor Water as a gas. You cannot see water vapor.

Think About What You Have Read

 **CRCT Prep**

❶ When drops of water in the air come together, they form

   A. water vapor.

   B. clouds.

   C. precipitation.   S2E3a

❷ What happens to water in the water cycle?

❸ List the seasons in the order in which they occur.

❹ Draw the same tree or plant in winter and spring. How are the drawings the same? How are they different?

KWL

What Did You Learn?

 **CRCT Prep**

❶ Circle the correct answer.

❷ In a water cycle, water

_____

_____

❸ Name the four seasons in order.

_____

❹ Draw a tree in winter and in spring.

What Do You Know?

Talk with a partner.

Make a list of things that you can see in the sky.

_____

_____

_____

Motions in the Sky

Contents

What Do You Want to Know?

What do you wonder about the Sun and the planets?

_____

_____

VOCABULARY

planet A large object that moves around the Sun. *(noun)*

solar system The Sun and the space objects that move around it. *(noun)*

Sun The brightest object in the day sky. *(noun)*

VOCABULARY ACTIVITY

Use Words

Sun

What words on pages 30 and 31 help you understand what the Sun is? Circle them.

GPS **S2E1a.** Describe the physical attributes of stars—size, brightness, and patterns.

1 What Makes Up the Solar System?

The **Sun** is the brightest thing in the day sky.
It is much larger than Earth.
The Sun looks small because it is very far away.

The Sun is made of hot gases.
The gases give off energy.
The Sun's energy comes to Earth
as light.
Some of the Sun's light is changed
to heat.

the Sun

1. Look at the picture on page 30.
   What tells you that the Sun is bright?

   _____

   _____

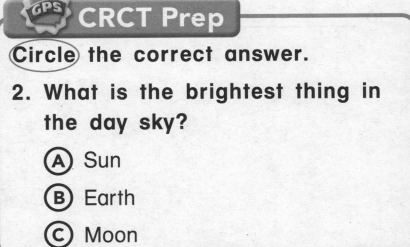

CRCT Prep

Circle the correct answer.

2. What is the brightest thing in
   the day sky?

   Ⓐ Sun

   Ⓑ Earth

   Ⓒ Moon

   S2E1a

31

3. Fill in the blanks.

a. The Sun helps plants

<u>live</u> and <u>grow</u> .

b. The Sun's light helps

<u>people</u> and <u>animals</u>

see.

4. Some of the Sun's light is changed

to <u>heat</u> .

Living things on Earth use energy from the Sun.

The Sun helps plants live and grow.

The Sun's light helps people and animals to see.

The Sun warms the land.
It warms the air.
It warms water.
The Sun keeps people and animals warm, too.

5. List four things that the Sun warms.

The air

The water

The land and people

I Wonder . . . Living things on Earth need the Sun. What are some of the ways in which people use the Sun?

_____

_____

_____

6. The Sun and the space objects that move around it make up the

_____.

7. Look at the drawing on pages 34 and 35. The space objects moving around the Sun are called

_____.

The Solar System

The Sun and the space objects that move around it make up our **solar system**.

A **planet** is a large object that moves around the Sun.

Our solar system has eight planets. Planets are always in the sky.

Jupiter

Saturn

Uranus

Neptune

Pluto
(dwarf planet)

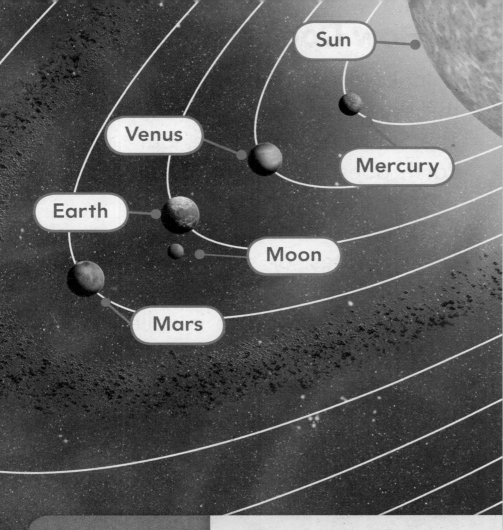

Main Idea

What makes up the solar system?

Summary

The Sun, which gives us heat and light, is the center of the solar system.

Circle the words on page 34 that tell what makes up our solar system.

▶ **Main Idea**   What makes up the solar system?

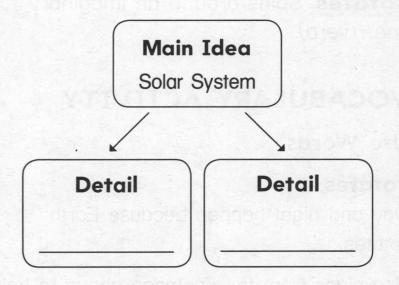

Main Idea
Solar System

Detail
_____

Detail
_____

VOCABULARY

orbit The path that one space object travels around another. *(noun)*

revolve To move in a path around an object. *(verb)*

rotates Spins around an imaginary line. *(verb)*

VOCABULARY ACTIVITY

Use Words

rotates

Day and night happen because Earth rotates.

Use clues from the sentence above to help you understand what the word **rotates** means.

36 **S2E2a.** Investigate the position of the sun in relation to a fixed object on earth at various times of the day.

2 How Does Earth Move?

It looks like the Sun moves across the sky each day.
The Sun does not move, but Earth does.

Earth Spins

Earth **rotates**, or spins around an imaginary line.
This make-believe line is called an axis.

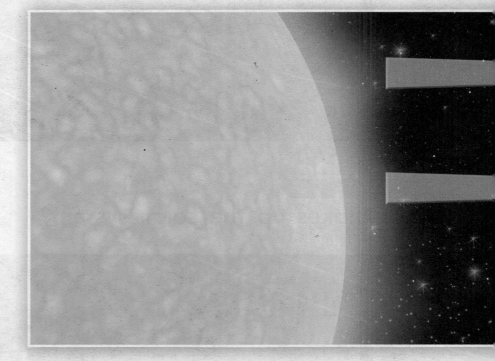

Different parts of Earth face the Sun as Earth rotates.
It is day on the part of Earth that faces the Sun.
It is night on the part of Earth that faces away from the Sun.
It takes Earth one day to rotate one time.

axis

1. Put an X on the part of Earth where it is day.

2. How long does it take the Earth to rotate one time?

_____

3. List two ways in which shadows change.

a. _____

b. _____

4. Circle the shadows on pages 38 and 39.

Shadows Change

Light from the Sun shines on Earth.
Shadows are made when something blocks the Sun's light.
Shadows change when Earth rotates.
Shadows change how long they are.
Shadows change where they are.

People can tell time by looking at the Sun and shadows.

Shadows Change

morning

The Sun is low in the sky.
Shadows are long.
Shadows get shorter and shorter until noon.

noon

The Sun is at its highest point in the sky.
Shadows are shortest.

afternoon

The Sun is low in the sky again.
Shadows grow longer.

CRCT Prep

Circle the correct answer.

5. When are shadows shortest?

Ⓐ morning

Ⓑ noon

Ⓒ afternoon

S2E2a

6. Use your finger to trace the path of Earth around the Sun. What is this path called?

_____

7. Find winter in the picture. Circle the correct words.

a. Georgia is tipped (toward / away from) the Sun.

b. Georgia gets (more light / less light) in winter than in summer.

Earth Moves Around the Sun

Earth moves in another way as it rotates.

Earth and the other planets **revolve**, or move in a path, around the Sun. The path that one space object travels around another is called an **orbit**.

It takes one year for Earth to revolve around the Sun.

The seasons change as Earth orbits the Sun.
The part of Earth tipped toward the Sun gets the most light.
It is summer there.
The part of Earth tipped away from the Sun gets less light.
It is winter there.

Draw Conclusions

If it is spring, how long will it be until it is spring again?

Summary   Earth moves in two different ways. It rotates and it revolves. What changes happen on Earth because the planet rotates?

_____

_____

_____

▶ **Draw Conclusions**   If it is spring, how long will it be until it is spring again?

A year has four seasons: spring, summer, fall, and winter.

↓

_____
_____

VOCABULARY

Moon A large sphere made of rock. *(noun)*

phases The different ways the Moon looks. *(noun)*

VOCABULARY ACTIVITY

Use Words

Moon

Circle the words on page 42 that describe the Moon.

3 # How Does the Moon Move?

The **Moon** is a large sphere made of rock.

It is the closest large space object to Earth.

It looks like the Moon moves across the sky at night.

This happens because Earth is rotating.

The Moon has mountains and craters, or pits. You can see dark spots on the Moon from Earth.

craters

  S2E2d. Use observations and charts to record the shape of the moon for a period of time.

The Moon in Motion

The Moon revolves in an orbit around Earth.

It takes about one month for the Moon to go around Earth one time. This happens month after month.

Earth

Moon

1. How does the Moon move?

_____

_____

2. Why does the Moon appear to move across the sky at night?

_____

_____

I Wonder . . . I know that the Moon does not always look the same. Why is the new Moon dark?

_____

_____

_____

_____

Circle the correct answer.

3. What causes Moon phases?

Ⓐ Earth rotating on its axis

Ⓑ Earth orbiting the Moon

Ⓒ the Moon orbiting Earth

S2E2d

The Changing Moon

The Moon does not have its own light.

It reflects the Sun's light.

The Sun shines on only one side of the Moon at a time.

You may only see part of the side of the Moon that is lighted as it revolves around Earth.

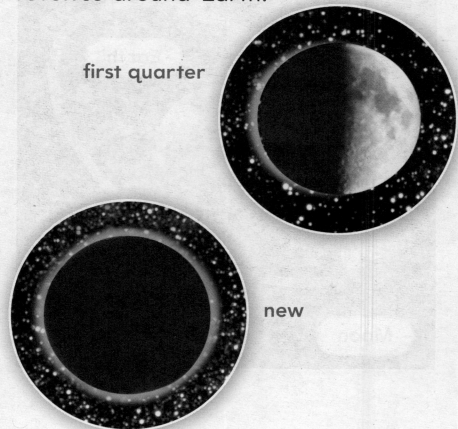

first quarter

new

The Moon looks a little different every night.
The different ways the Moon looks are called **phases**.

full

last quarter

Cause and Effect

Why does the Moon look bright in the night sky?

Summary   The Moon is a large sphere of rock that orbits Earth.

Draw and label the four phases of the Moon.

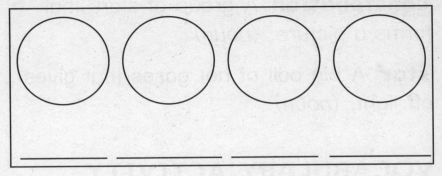

_____ _____ _____ _____

▶ **Cause and Effect**   Why does the Moon look bright in the night sky?

Cause	Effect
_____	The Moon looks bright.
_____	

VOCABULARY

constellation A group of stars that forms a picture. (*noun*)

star A big ball of hot gases that gives off light. (*noun*)

VOCABULARY ACTIVITY

Use Pictures

star

Say the word aloud.

Use clues from the pictures to help you understand what the word **star** means.

GPS **S2E1a.** Describe the physical attributes of stars—size, brightness, and patterns.

4 What Stars Can You See?

A **star** is a big ball of hot gases that gives off light.
Stars are always in the sky.
The Sun is the closest star to Earth.
The Sun's light is very bright.
You cannot see other stars during the day.

Stars are different colors.

blue star

red star

You can see other stars at night when the sky is dark.
Other stars are very large, just like the Sun.
These stars look small because they are very far away.
Some stars look brighter than others.
Those stars may be bigger, hotter, or closer to Earth.

The Sun is a yellow star.

yellow star

white star

Circle the correct answer.

1. **What color star is our Sun?**

   Ⓐ red

   Ⓑ white

   Ⓒ yellow

   S2E1a

2. Stars are very large. Why do they look small in the night sky?

   _____

   _____

47

3. Underline the meaning of constellation on page 48.

I Wonder . . . Could I make up my own constellations?

_____

_____

_____

Star Patterns

Some stars look like they make pictures.

A **constellation** is a group of stars that forms a picture. Constellations have names. Constellations can help you find some stars.

The star Polaris is in the Little Dipper. Polaris is also called the North Star.

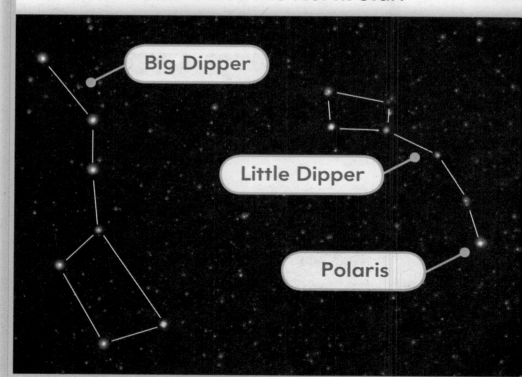

Big Dipper

Little Dipper

Polaris

Star Locations

It looks like stars move across the night sky.

This happens because Earth is spinning.

You see different parts of the night sky as Earth rotates.

The Little Dipper looks like it's moving because Earth is moving.

Compare and Contrast

How is the Sun different from other stars?

Summary

You can see stars in the night sky. Why do stars seem to move across the night sky?

_____

▶ **Compare and Contrast**   How is the Sun different from other stars?

	Sun	Other Stars
How far away?	_____ _____	_____ _____
When can it be seen?	_____ _____	_____ _____

(Circle) the science words that have two syllables.

Draw and label a picture of an object that you see in the night sky.

constellation A group of stars that forms a picture.

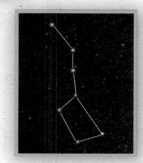

Moon A large sphere made of rock.

orbit The path that one space object travels around another.

phases The different ways the moon looks.

planet A large object that moves around the Sun.

revolve To move in a path around an object.

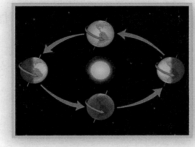

rotates Spins around an imaginary line.

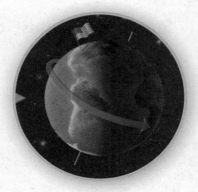

Use the word rotates in a sentence.

_____

_____

Visit www.eduplace.com/gascp to play puzzles and word games.

Fill in the web with words related to stars.

move   constellations   small

seem to _____ because Earth moves

Stars

look _____ because they are far away

can form pictures called _____

solar system The Sun and the space objects that move around it.

star A big ball of hot gases that gives off light.

Sun The brightest object in the day sky.

Think About What You Have Read

 **CRCT Prep**

❶ Stars in the night sky look smaller than our Sun because

   A. they are farther away from Earth.

   B. they are closer to Earth than our Sun.

   C. they can be seen during the day.   **S2E1a**

❷ What causes night and day on Earth?

❸ Why do some stars look brighter than others?

❹ How does the Sun help living things?

K W L

What Did You Learn?

 **CRCT Prep**

❶ Circle the correct answer.

❷ _____ causes night and day on Earth.

❸ Some stars look brighter than others

because _____

_____.

❹ The Sun helps living things

_____ and

_____.

What Do You Know?

Talk with a partner.

Draw an object.

Describe the object.

Comparing Matter

Contents

What do you want to know about matter?

_____

_____

How can you compare different objects?

_____

_____

_____

55

VOCABULARY

gas A state of matter that spreads out to fill a space. (*noun*)

liquid A state of matter that does not have its own shape. (*noun*)

mass The amount of matter in an object. (*noun*)

properties Color, shape, size, odor, and texture. (*noun*)

solid A state of matter that has its own size and shape. (*noun*)

volume The amount of space a liquid takes up. (*noun*)

1 How Can You Compare Matter?

You can tell about something by telling about its properties.
Color, shape, size, odor, and texture are **properties**.
Odor tells how something smells.
Texture tells how something feels.

A balloon can be red or yellow.

A slipper can be soft and fuzzy.

A penny is round and flat.

You can tell about a thing by telling what materials were used to make it. For example, a penny is made of copper.

Marbles are made of glass.

These toy dinosaurs are made of plastic.

1. What are some properties that you can use to describe an object?

a. color

b. shape

c. texture

d. size

2. What property do the penny and the marbles share?

They are both small

3. (Circle) the object that light can pass through.

4. Label one object on this page with an A. Label another object on this page with a B.

   a. List the properties of object A.

   _____

   _____

   b. List the properties of object B.

   _____

   _____

Other properties tell what something does.
Some things sink in water.
Other things float.
Some properties tell what the materials do.
Some things bend.
Other things break.
Some materials let light pass through.

This rock will sink in water.

A pencil will float in water.

Light can pass through these.

This toy can bend.

States of Matter

All things are made of matter.
The three states of matter are solid, liquid, and gas.
A **solid** is a state of matter that has its own size and shape.
A solid keeps its shape and size even if it is moved.

A toy boat keeps its size and shape when you put it in water.

5. What are three states of matter?

   a. _solid_

   b. _liquid/water_

   c. _gas_

6. Put an X on something in the picture that is not a solid.

7. Underline the words that describe a liquid.

I Wonder . . . I know that water is a liquid. I know that a liquid does not have its own shape. What shape is the water in the pool?

_____

_____

A **liquid** is a state of matter that does not have its own shape. Liquids flow. They take the shape of what holds them.

Juice takes the shape of the pitcher and glasses it is put in.

liquid

A **gas** is a state of matter that spreads out to fill a space.
A gas does not have its own shape.
It always fills a closed container.
The gas comes out when the container is opened.

A balloon holds a gas.

The beach ball holds a gas.

8. You cannot see the air inside a balloon. How do you know it is there?

The air make the balloon round

9. Compare the gas in the beach ball with the liquid in the pool. How are they alike?

Both take the shape of thr con tainer

10. How do you measure the volume of a liquid?

_____

CRCT Prep

(Circle) the correct answer.

11. What would you use to measure how much space a solid takes up?

Ⓐ a measuring cup

Ⓑ a milk carton

Ⓒ a ruler

S2P1

62

Using Tools to Measure

All matter takes up space. You can measure how much space matter takes up.

You can use a ruler to measure how long a solid is.

You can use a ruler to measure how wide or how high a solid is, too.

You can use a measuring cup to measure the amount of space that a liquid takes up, or **volume**.

You pour a liquid into a measuring cup to find its volume.

All matter has mass.
Mass is the amount of matter in an object.
You can use a balance to measure the mass of something.

Classify

Name two properties that can be measured.

Put the object you want to measure on one side of the balance.

Add mass units until the sides are even.

balance

Summary

You can describe objects by their properties. Do all liquids, gases, and solids have mass?

▶ **Classify** Name two properties that can be measured.

Properties You Can Measure		
Ruler	Measuring Cup	Balance

VOCABULARY

mixture Something made of two or more things. *(noun)*

separate To take apart. *(verb)*

dissolves Mixes completely with water. *(verb)*

VOCABULARY ACTIVITY

Use Syllables

separate

Break the word into syllables.

Say each syllable aloud.

Clap once for each syllable.

How many syllables does this word have?

_____

GPS **S2P1b.** Investigate changes in objects by tearing, dissolving, melting, squeezing, etc.

2 How Does Matter Change?

A **mixture** is something made of two or more things.
You can put matter together to make a mixture.
There is no new matter in a mixture.

Trail mix is a mixture.
It is easy to separate.

You can take apart, or **separate**, a mixture.
Each part is still there.
Some mixtures are easy to separate.
The parts stay the same.
The parts are easy to see.

Trail Mix
2 cups cereal
1 cup raisins
1 cup peanuts
1 cup dry fruit

1. Circle the mixture on these pages. Put an X on the parts that make up the mixture.

2. List the parts that make up the trail mix.

a. cereal

b. dry fruit

c. Peanut

d. raisins

I Wonder . . . What other mixture is hard to separate?

Coffee, cake, gatorade

3. Circle the word that makes the sentence true.

When you stir drink mix powder into water, the powder (separates, dissolves) in the water.

Some mixtures are hard to separate. When you stir drink mix powder with water, it **dissolves**, or mixes completely with the water.

The powder breaks into small bits that are too small to see. But it is still powder.

The drink mix powder dissolves in the water.

4. Tell whether each mixture would be hard or easy to separate.

Mixture	Hard or Easy
salad	easy
glue	Hard
collection of seashells	easy
hot chocolate	hard

5. Look at the pictures on these two pages. List three ways to change solid matter.

a. _____

b. _____

c. _____

6. How can you change a sheet of paper?

_____

_____

Changing Matter

You can change solid matter in many ways.

You can cut matter to change its shape.

You can break matter into smaller pieces to change its size or shape.

cutting paper

You can pound clay to make it flat.
You can sand wood to make it smooth.
These kinds of changes do not change the material that the matter is made of.

pounding clay

sanding wood

Circle the correct answer.

7. Cutting, sanding, and pounding can change the shape of

Ⓐ solids.

Ⓑ liquids.

Ⓒ gases.

S2P1b

69

8. Some liquids change to _solid_ when you take away heat.

9. Some solids change to _liquid_ when you add heat.

Changing States

Matter can change from one state to another.
Some liquids can change to solids when you take away heat.
Other solids can change to liquids when you add heat.

The juice in the pitcher is a liquid.
The juice in the tray is a solid.
The juice on the plate is changing from a solid to a liquid.

All matter does not change the same way when you heat it. Some things melt fast. Some things melt slowly. Other things do not melt at all.

Draw Conclusions

If a solid changes to a liquid, what can you say happened?

Butter melts fast.

Summary
Matter can be changed in many different ways. If you add a small amount of heat to ice and to a plastic toy, which item would melt faster?

_____

▶ **Draw Conclusions** If a solid changes to a liquid, what can you say happened?

Fact: Matter can change from one state to another.

Fact: Some solids can change to _____ when you add _____.

Conclusion: _____

VOCABULARY

magnify To make objects look larger. *(verb)*

VOCABULARY ACTIVITY

Use Words

In the picture on this page, the children

are using a _____ to magnify the small parts of matter.

3 How Does Matter Look Up Close?

Matter is made of very small parts. The parts are too little to see with only your eyes.
You can use a tool to see these small parts.

The children are using a hand lens.

hand lens

  S2P1. Students will investigate the properties of matter and changes that occur in objects.

Tools that Magnify

Some tools can make objects look larger, or **magnify** them.
A hand lens can make objects look bigger.
A microscope can magnify objects even more.

Scientists use microscopes to magnify objects.

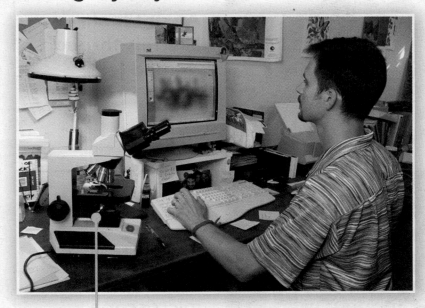

microscope

1. Circle the hand lens.
2. Circle the microscope.
3. What do these tools do?

_____

_____

Circle the correct answer.

4. Compared to a hand lens, an ant magnified under the microscope looks

Ⓐ bigger.

Ⓑ smaller.

Ⓒ the same size.

S2P1

5. Draw lines. Match each object to what it might look like when magnified.

flower

clothing

insect

74

Ants Up Close

Ants look like this without a magnifying tool.

An ant looks like this through a hand lens.

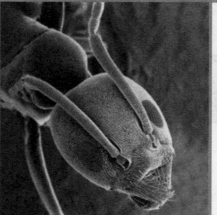

An ant looks like this through a microscope.

Matter Up Close

You can see the small parts of matter when you use a tool to magnify an object.

feather

fish scales

sugar cube

strawberry

Main Idea and Details

Why are tools needed to see small parts of matter?

Summary

Matter is made of parts too small to see with only your eyes.

What might you learn by magnifying a grasshopper?

_____

▶ **Main Idea** Why are tools needed to see small parts of matter?

Main Idea
Tools help you see small parts of matter.

Detail	**Detail**
Some tools make objects look _____.	Some tools help you see _____.

A _____ and a _____ take the shape of their containers.

(Circle) the two science words that fit.

solid

liquid

gas

dissolves Mixes completely with water.

gas A state of matter that spreads out to fill a space. A gas fills the inside of a balloon.

liquid A state of matter that does not have its own shape.

Think About What You Have Read

CRCT Prep

❶ Something made of two or more things is a _____

   A. property.

   B. volume.

   C. mixture.

S2P1

❷ What two tools can help you see small parts of things?

❸ What is a solid?

❹ Why are some mixtures harder to separate than others?

K W L

What Did You Learn?

CRCT Prep

❶ Circle the correct answer.

❷ A _____ and a _____ can help you see small parts of things.

❸ A solid is

_____

_____

❹ Some mixtures are harder to separate than others because

_____

_____

What Do You Know?

Talk with a partner.

What kinds of things move?

_____

_____

Objects in Motion

Contents

What do you wonder about how things move?

_____

_____

What do you want to know about forces?

_____

_____

What do you want to know about motion?

_____

_____

VOCABULARY

position A place or location. *(noun)*

motion Moving from one place to another. *(noun)*

gravity A pull toward the center of Earth. Objects fall to the ground unless something holds them up. *(noun)*

VOCABULARY ACTIVITY

Use Words

position

What words on page 82 help you understand what **position** means? Circle them.

1 How Do Things Move?

You can tell about an object by telling about its position.
Position is a place or location.
Position words help you talk about where an object is.
These words compare where two objects are.

to the left of the piggy bank

on the desk

under the piggy bank and over the books

S2P3a. Demonstrate how pushing and pulling an object affects the motion of the object.

above the bed

on top of the bed

next to the bed

1. Describe the position of the pillow.

_____

2. What is another way to describe the position of the table?

_____

GPS **CRCT Prep**

Circle the correct answer.

3. What is the place or location of objects called?

Ⓐ motion

Ⓑ position

Ⓒ friction

S2P3a

83

4. <u>Underline</u> the words that describe different kinds of motion.

5. Draw an arrow on the picture to show the swing's motion.

I Wonder . . . I know that there are different kinds of motion. How do the parts of my body move when I run?

_____

_____

_____

_____

Changing Position

Something that is in **motion** changes its position.
It moves from one place to another.
How can you tell if something is moving?
You can compare its position to things around it.
There are different kinds of motion.
Things can move in a straight line.
Things can move in a circle.

This girl is moving back and forth.

How will this ball move next?

Things can move up
and down.
What happens when you
let go of something you
are holding?
It drops to the ground!
This change in position is
caused by gravity.
Gravity is a pull toward the
center of Earth.

Draw Conclusions

Does a baseball move in a straight
line or a circle when hit?

Summary   An object that is in motion changes its position or moves from one place to another. What will happen after a basketball is thrown through the hoop?

_____

▶ **Draw Conclusions**

Does a baseball move in a straight line or a circle when hit?

Fact

A baseball is hit by the bat.

↓

Fact

A baseball is in motion.

↓

Conclusion

_____

VOCABULARY

force A push or a pull. *(noun)*

friction A force that makes an object slow down when it rubs against another object. *(noun)*

VOCABULARY ACTIVITY

Use Words

When you push a wheelbarrow, you are using **force.**

Use clues from the sentence above to help you understand what the word **force** means.

_____

_____

S2P3a. Demonstrate how pushing and pulling an object affects the motion of the object.

2 What Do Forces Do?

You use force to move something.
A **force** is a push or a pull.
A large force moves something heavy.
A small force moves something light.
When you push or pull something, you give it energy.
Big things need more energy to move than small things.

This needs a large push.

This needs a small push.

A large force gives something more energy.
Try to kick a ball with a lot of force.
The ball moves fast and goes far.
Kick the same ball with less force.
The ball goes slow and not as far.

Which kick will make the ball go farther?

1. How can pushes and pulls change an object's motion? Give an example.

   _____

   _____

2. Fill in the diagram about pushes and pulls.

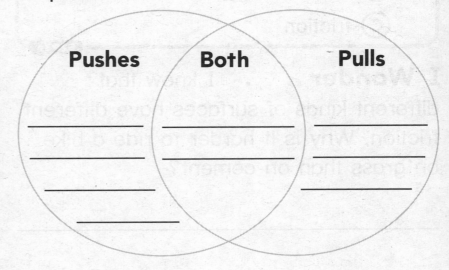

   Pushes   **Both**   **Pulls**

3. If you kick a ball with a small force, will it go a short distance or a long distance?

   _____

87

Circle the correct answer.

4. What makes a moving object slow down?

Ⓐ motion

Ⓑ gravity

Ⓒ friction

S2P3a

I Wonder . . . I know that different kinds of surfaces have different friction. Why is it harder to ride a bike on grass than on cement?

_____

_____

_____

_____

Friction and Motion

Friction is a force.
Friction makes one thing slow down when it rubs against another thing.
Bike tires rub against the road when you ride your bike.
The rubbing causes friction.

| cement | grass | gravel |

Riding on a rough surface causes a lot of friction.
Riding on a smooth surface causes less friction.

Changing Direction

Forces can change the direction of something that is moving.
You push a ball with your hand to bounce it.
The ball moves down until it hits the ground.
Then it changes direction and bounces back up.

Cause and Effect

What will happen to the basketball if you push harder on it?

Summary   A force can start, slow down, or stop the motion of an object.

How can gravity change the direction of an object?

_____

_____

▶ Cause and Effect

What will happen to the basketball if you push harder on it?

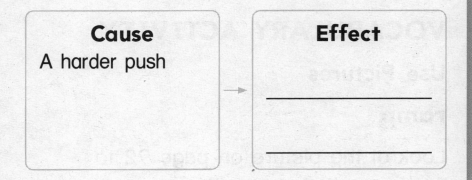

Cause	Effect
A harder push	_____ _____

VOCABULARY

simple machine A tool that can make it easier to move objects. *(noun)*

ramp A slanted tool used to move things from one level to another. *(noun)*

lever A bar that moves around a fixed point. *(noun)*

pulley A wheel with a groove through which a rope or chain moves. *(noun)*

VOCABULARY ACTIVITY

Use Pictures

ramp

Look at the picture on page 92 to understand what **ramp** means.

3 What Can You Do with Motion?

Motion can be measured in different ways.

Measuring Motion

You can measure how far something goes.
You can measure the time it takes to get there, too.
It takes more time to go farther.
You can measure the time it takes to swim a certain distance.

Fastest Swimming Times

Distance	Time
50 meters	about 22 seconds
100 meters	about 48 seconds

A swimmer who wins a race goes the fastest.
The swimmer may be kicking faster.
Moving faster means that it will take less time to go a certain distance.

Which swimmer moved faster?

1. What are two ways to measure motion?

   a. _____

   b. _____

2. On page 91, (circle) the swimmer who is swimming faster.

3. Use the chart on page 90 to answer the following questions.

   a. How are the distances ordered?

   _____

   b. How are the times listed?

   _____

   c. What can you infer from the chart about time and distance?

   _____

   _____

91

I Wonder . . . Why is it easier to push a heavy object down a ramp than up a ramp?

_____

_____

_____

_____

_____

_____

Using Ramps

A **simple machine** is a tool that can make it easier to move things.

A **ramp** is a simple machine.

It is used to move things from one level to another.

You can move something heavy when you use a ramp.

It takes less force to move things up a ramp than to lift them up.

Using Levers

A **lever** is a bar that moves around a fixed point.

A lever can change the direction of a motion.

Different kinds of levers are used for different jobs.

This man is pushing down on one end of a screwdriver. The other end will lift up the lid of the can.

4. How does a lever make it easier to do work?

_____

_____

5. Draw an arrow to show the direction the man's hand is moving.

6. Draw an arrow to show the direction the lid is moving.

Circle the correct answer.

7. What is a tool that can be used to make it easier to move objects?

(A) simple machine

(B) friction

(C) speed

S2P3b

Summary   A simple machine is a tool that can make it easier to move objects.

How can a pulley make it easier to move an object?

_____

_____

_____

▶ **Compare and Contrast**   How are all simple machines alike?

_____

_____

pulley

Using Pulleys

A pulley is another machine that lifts things. A **pulley** is a wheel that is turned by a rope or chain.
To lift something, you pull down on the rope. The rope on the other side goes up.
A pulley changes the direction of a force.

Compare and Contrast

How are all simple machines alike?

force A push or a pull.

friction A force that makes an object slow down when it rubs against another object.

gravity A pull toward the center of Earth. Objects fall to the ground unless something holds them up.

Fill in the blanks with science words.

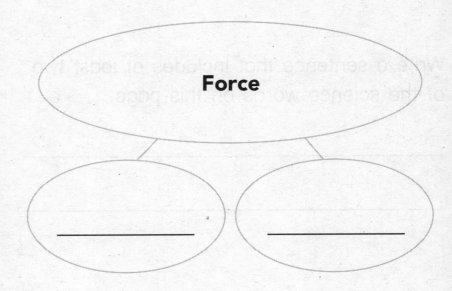

Force

_____   _____

Visit www.eduplace.com to play puzzles and word games.

Write a sentence that includes at least two of the science words on this page.

_____

_____

lever A bar that moves around a fixed point.

motion Moving from one place to another.

position A place or location.

pulley A wheel with a groove through which a rope or chain moves.

ramp A slanted tool used to move things from one level to another.

simple machine A tool that can make it easier to move objects.

Fill in the word web.

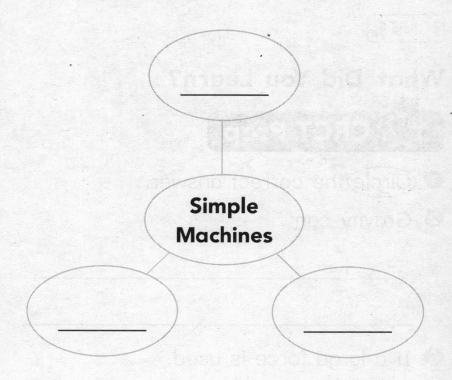

Simple Machines

What Did You Learn?

1 (Circle) the correct answer.

2 Gravity can

_____

_____

3 If a large force is used,

_____

_____

4 More than one position word can be used to tell about an object because

_____

_____

Think About What You Have Read

1 What is a slanted tool used to move things from one level to another?

A. friction
B. force
C. ramp

S2P3b

2 How can gravity make something move?

3 How will something move when a large force is used?

4 More than one position word can be used to tell about an object. Why?

What Do You Know?

Talk with a partner. List things that give off heat and light. Circle the ones that you see in your classroom.

_____

_____

_____

_____

_____

_____

_____

_____

100

Heat and Light

Contents

What Do You Want to Know?

What do you wonder about heat and light?

_____

_____

_____

_____

_____

_____

_____

VOCABULARY

heat A kind of energy that makes things warm. *(noun)*

melt To change from a solid to a liquid. *(verb)*

VOCABULARY ACTIVITY

Use Words

heat

Heat from the Sun melted the ice.

Use clues from the sentence to help you understand what the word **heat** means.

1 What Is Heat?

Heat makes things warm.
It is a kind of energy.
More heat makes things hot.
Less heat makes things cool.

Heat from a fire keeps you warm.

S2P2a. Identify sources of light energy, heat energy, and energy of motion.
S2P2b. Describe how light, heat, and motion energy are used.

We get heat from many things.
The Sun gives Earth its heat.
Heat from the Sun is important
to living things.

Sun shining in Georgia.

1. Tell what happens when heat is added or taken away.

   a. When heat is added,

   _____.

   b. When heat is taken away,

   _____.

2. List two things that give off heat.

   a. _____

   b. _____

3. Look at the pictures on pages 104 and 105. (Circle) all the objects that are giving off heat.

We get heat from fuel such as wood.

We get heat from lamps and heaters.
We get heat from stoves and toasters, too.

toaster

The toaster heats the bread to make toast.

I Wonder . . . Can we get heat from both natural and human-made objects?

_____

_____

_____

_____

_____

4. List three ways that people use heat.

a. _____

b. _____

c. _____

CRCT Prep

Circle the correct answers.

5. To dry her hair, what kind of energy is the girl using?

Ⓐ light.

Ⓑ heat.

Ⓒ motion.

S2P2a

How Heat Is Used

People use heat in many ways.
We use heat to warm our homes.
We use heat to cook our food.
We use heat to dry our clothes.

We use heat to
dry our hair.

106

Heat changes things.
When something that is frozen is heated, it melts.
To **melt** is to change from a solid to a liquid.

Main Idea and Details

What are three sources of heat?

Summary   Heat is a kind of energy that makes things warm. The Sun, stoves, and toasters are sources of heat. Heat can be used in different ways.

How is heat changing the snowball?

▶ **Main Idea and Details**   What are three sources of heat? Circle the heat sources.

Main Idea

There are many sources of heat.

Detail	**Detail**	**Detail**

VOCABULARY

light A kind of energy that you can see. *(noun)*

VOCABULARY ACTIVITY

Use Words

light

Look at the picture on this page. Circle the object that is giving off **light**.

2 What Is Light?

Light is a kind of energy you can see.
Light comes from many things.
Earth gets light from the Sun.

The Sun gives us lots of light.

S2P2a. Identify sources of light energy, heat energy, and energy of motion.
S2P2b. Describe how light, heat, and motion energy are used.

Fires and candles give off light when they burn.
The light bulbs inside flashlights and lamps give off light too.

1. List sources of light.

```
         Sources of Light
          /            \
         /              \
Sources in          Sources with
  Nature               Bulbs

a. _____     c. _____


b. _____     d. _____
```

2. (Circle) the sources of light shown on pages 110 and 111.

I Wonder . . . How would Earth be different if it did not get light and heat energy from the Sun?

_____

_____

_____

_____

_____

_____

How Light Is Used

You need light for many things. Light helps you see.

Light keeps us safe when we drive or walk.
Stoplights tell us when to stop or go.

Circle the correct answer.

3. People use light

Ⓐ to see.

Ⓑ to melt ice.

Ⓒ to warm things.

S2P2b

Summary   There are many sources of light, including the Sun. How does light help keep people safe?

_____

_____

_____

▶ **Cause and Effect**   What are three sources of light? (Circle) the pictures that are light sources.

Lighthouses keep boats safe. The light from lighthouses can be seen from far away.

Lighthouses keep boats away from rocks along the shore.

Cause and Effect

What are three sources of light?

heat A kind of energy that makes things warm.

light A kind of energy that you can see.

melt To change from a solid to a liquid.

Visit www.eduplace.com/gascp to play word games and puzzles.

Choose two science words. Write each word three times.

_____   _____

_____   _____

_____   _____

What Did You Learn?

❶ (Circle) the correct answer.

❷ Earth gets most of its heat from

_____.

❸ Three things in my home that give off light are

_____

_____

❹ The kitchen is warmer because

_____

_____

_____.

Responding

Think About What You Have Read

❶ **A kind of energy that makes things warm is**

A. light.

B. melt.

C. heat.

S2P2b

❷ Where does Earth get most of its heat from?

❸ Name three things in your home that give off light.

❹ Bread is baking in the oven. Why is the kitchen warmer than other rooms in your house?

What Do You Know?

Talk with a partner. List different plants you know. What parts do these plants have?

_____

_____

_____

_____

_____

Plant Life Cycles

Contents

What Do You Want to Know?

What do you wonder about how plants grow?

_____

_____

_____

_____

_____

_____

_____

VOCABULARY

cone The part of a plant where seeds form in plants without flowers. *(noun)*

flower The part of a plant where fruit and seeds form. *(noun)*

fruit The part of a flower that is around a seed. *(noun)*

life cycle The series of changes that a living thing goes through as it grows. *(noun)*

seed The part of a plant from which a new plant grows. *(noun)*

1 How Do Plants Change During Their Life Cycles?

A plant has many parts.
Some parts help plants make new plants.
Some plants have flowers.
Flowers have fruit and seeds.
A **fruit** is the part around a seed.
A **seed** is where a new plant grows.

flower

Almond Tree

 S2L1c. Investigate the life cycle of a plant by growing a plant from a seed and by recording changes over a period of time.

Some trees have flowers.
The flowers have seeds inside.
You can plant the seeds.
They will grow into new plants!

fruit

seed

1. What plant part makes new plants?

_____

2. Draw a flower.

3. What happens during the life cycle of a plant?

_____

_____

4. Circle all the seeds on pages 120 and 121.

Plant Life Cycles

Living things grow and change.
Living things die, too.
Many changes happen as a living thing grows.
All of these changes are its **life cycle**.

A pea is a seed. It grows into a pea plant.

Plants have different life cycles.
Most plants start from a seed.
The seed needs warm air and water.
Then it grows into a plant.

seeds

6. List fruits that have seeds.

_____

_____

_____

7. What does a seed need to grow?

_____

_____

_____

8. How many changes are shown in the life cycle of a tomato plant?

_____

I Wonder . . . I know that plants have life cycles. What happens after a plant dies?

_____

_____

_____

_____

The plant grows and changes. It grows leaves and flowers.

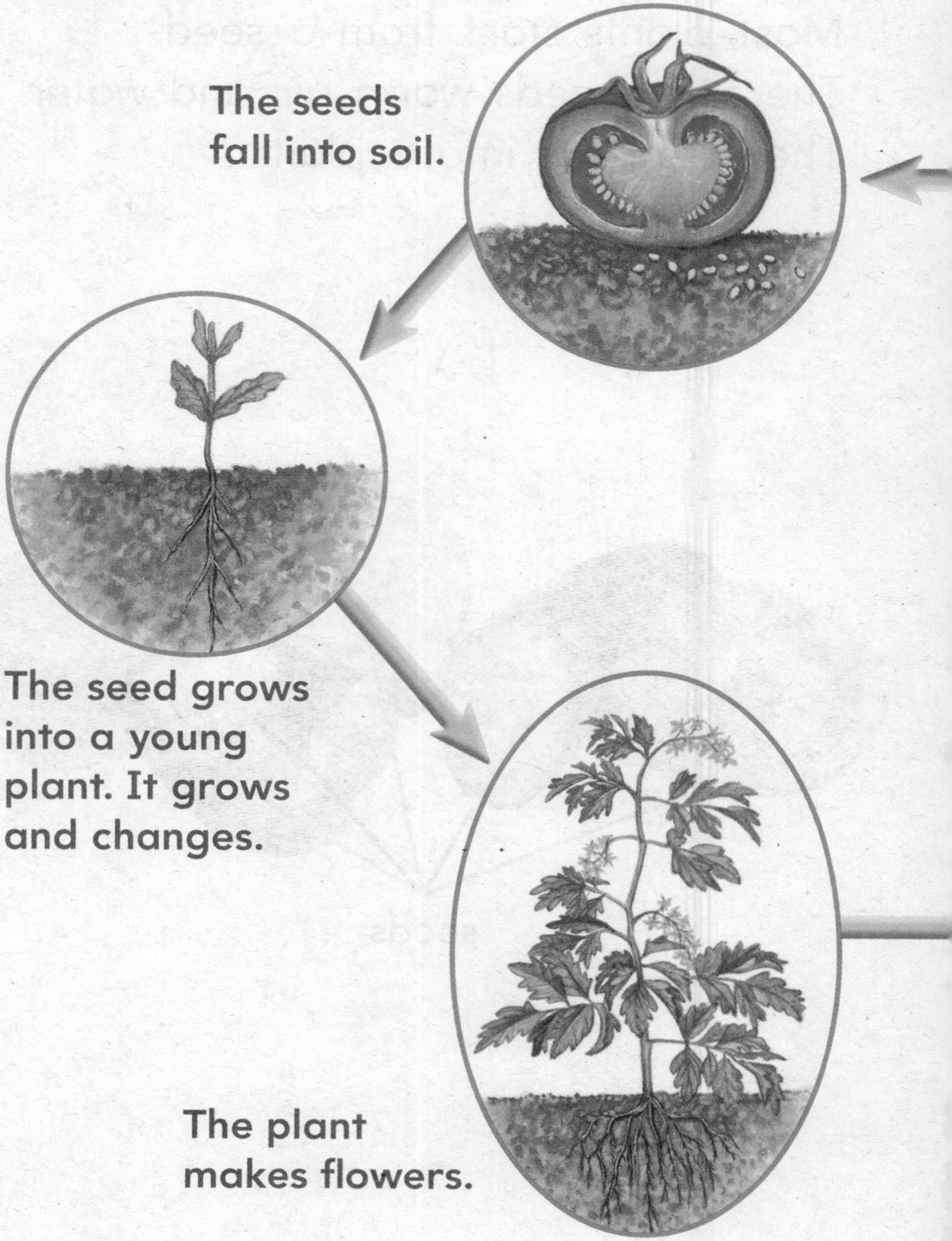

The seeds fall into soil.

The seed grows into a young plant. It grows and changes.

The plant makes flowers.

The plant dies. The seeds may grow into new plants.

Flowers make fruit. Seeds grow in the fruit.

The flowers make new seeds.
The seeds can grow into new plants.
The life cycle starts again.

9. Order the pictures of this life cycle. Write a number under each picture to show the correct order.

_____   _____

_____   _____

_____

10. Look at the pictures.
(Circle) the part of each plant
that makes seeds. Name these
plant parts.

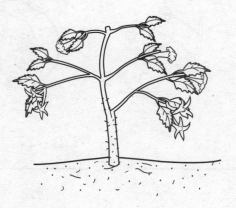

Life Cycle of a Pine Tree

Some plants do not have flowers
and fruit.
They have cones.

The seeds fall
into soil.

The seed grows
into a young
tree. It grows
and changes.

A **cone** is like a fruit.
It has seeds.
The cone keeps the seeds safe.

The tree makes cones.

Seeds grow in the cones.

The seeds may grow into new trees.

Sequence

How does a pine tree change as it grows?

Summary Plants grow and change in different ways. How do tomato plants change?

_____

_____

▶ **Sequence** How does a pine tree change as it grows?

↓

The pine tree makes cones.

↓

↓

VOCABULARY

inherit To have traits passed on from the parents. (*verb*)

VOCABULARY ACTIVITY

Use Syllables

inherit

Break the word into syllables.
Say each syllable aloud.
Clap once for each syllable.
How many syllables does **inherit** have?

_____

  S2L1c. Investigate the life cycle of a plant by growing a plant from a seed and by recording changes over a period of time.

2 What Kind of a Plant Grows from a Seed?

A parent plant makes seeds. The seeds grow into new plants. The new plants look like the parent plant.

This new plant will look like its parent.

A trait is the way something looks.
Color, shape, and size are traits.
All living things get traits from
their parents.
They inherit the traits.
Inherit means to have something
passed on.

**Living things inherit traits
from their parents.**

I. Look at the picture.
What traits might these plants have
inherited from their parents?

_____

_____

_____

GPS **CRCT Prep**

Circle the correct answer.

2. **All living things get their traits
from their**

Ⓐ sisters.

Ⓑ parents.

Ⓒ brothers.

S2L1c

3. Draw a picture of a new plant that could grow from one of the plants on this page.

These flowers inherited the same traits.
They have the same leaf shape.
They have the same flower color.
They will grow to be the same size.

Oak Trees and Acorns

Oak trees grow fruit called acorns.
The acorns have seeds.
Acorns fall to the ground.
They can grow into new plants.

acorns

I Wonder . . . I know that an acorn grows into an oak tree. What do maple seeds grow into?

_____

Summary A parent plant makes new plants with inherited traits. How is a new yellow tulip plant like its parent plant?

_____

_____

▶ Draw Conclusions What kinds of plants always grow from acorns?

Fact

↓

Fact
Acorns are seeds.

↓

Conclusion

The new plants look like the parent plant.
New plants look like each other, too.
They are all oak trees.
They have flat leaves.
The new plants will grow acorns, too.

oak tree

Draw Conclusions

What kinds of plants always grow from acorns?

How Do Plants of the Same Kind Differ?

3

New plants may look the same.
They may look a little different
because they can inherit
different traits.
They may be different sizes.
They may be different colors.

These berries
inherit color from
the parent plant.

VOCABULARY

environment All the living and
nonliving things around a living thing.
(noun)

population A group of the same kind
of living thing in one place. *(noun)*

VOCABULARY ACTIVITY

Use Syllables

environment

Break the word into syllables. Say each
syllable aloud. Clap once for each
syllable.
How many syllables are in the word
environment?

_____

 S2L1c. Investigate the life cycle of a plant by growing a plant from a seed and by
recording changes over a period of time.

I Wonder . . . The picture on this page shows two plants of the same kind. Why do the plants look different?

_____

_____

New plants may look a little different because of their environment, too. An **environment** is everything around a living thing. There are living things in an environment. There are nonliving things, too.

This plant got the right amount of sunlight.

This plant did not.

Differences in a Bigger Group

A **population** is a group of the same kind of living thing in one place.

Look at a population.

You can see ways plants are different.

a population of petunias

2. Tell how plants in this population are different.

_____

_____

3. Draw a petunia that would be part of this population.

Summary New plants that grow from seeds from the same parent may inherit different traits. How are these daffodils alike?

_____

_____

▶ **Compare and Contrast**
How might plants of a population be the same and different?

Compare	Contrast

These flowers are daffodils.
All the daffodils in a garden are a population.
The daffodils may not look the same.
They may be different colors.
They may be different sizes.
But they are all daffodils.

a population of daffodils

Compare and Contrast

How might plants of a population be the same and different?

How Do Plants React to Their Environment?

4

Gravity pulls all things toward each other.
Gravity changes plants.
It makes the roots of a plant grow down.

Gravity makes roots grow down.

VOCABULARY

gravity A force that pulls objects toward each other. *(noun)*

VOCABULARY ACTIVITY

Use Words

gravity

The ball falls to the ground because of gravity.
Use clues from the sentence above to help you understand what the word **gravity** means.

 S2L1c. Investigate the life cycle of a plant by growing a plant from a seed and by recording changes over a period of time.

1. The leaves of this plant are _____

   because it is being _____.
   Why?

   _____

   _____

   _____

2. What might touch this plant that
   would harm it?

   _____

   _____

   _____

Some plants are changed by touch, too.
If you touch this plant, it will close its leaves.
This keeps the plant safe.

Touch makes this plant close its leaves.

Plants need sunlight.
Some plants grow toward the light.
They bend toward the Sun.
You can turn your plants each day.
This helps them grow straight.

Some plants grow toward light.

Circle the correct answer.

3. **Look at the picture.**

How does sunlight affect plants?

(A) Plants grow toward the light.

(B) Plants grow away from the light.

(C) Plants are not affected by the light.

S2L1c

4. What can you do to help a plant grow straight?

_____

_____

5. Why is this tree growing this way?

_____

_____

_____

Weather Affects Plants

Weather can change how plants grow.
Wind can make plants fall over.
It can even change the shape of a tree.

This tree was bent by wind.

Plants need warm weather.
They can die if it is too hot or cold.
Plants need water, too.
They can die if they have too much
or too little water.

It is too cold for this plant.

Cause and Effect

How can weather change how
plants grow?

Summary Gravity, light, and touch can change how a plant grows.
How can the environment change plants?

_____

_____

▶**Cause and Effect** How can
weather change how plants grow?

Cause		Effect
	→	

139

(Circle) the science words that name parts of a plant.

Unscramble this word. **neco**

_____

cone The part of a plant where seeds form in plants without flowers.

environment All the living and nonliving things around a living thing.

flower The part of a plant where fruit and seeds form.

fruit The part of a flower that is around a seed.

gravity A force that pulls all objects toward each other.

Glossary

inherit To have traits passed on from the parent.

life cycle The series of changes that a living thing goes through as it grows.

population A group of the same kind of living thing in one place.

seed The part of a plant from which a new plant grows.

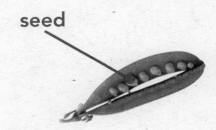

seed

 Visit www.eduplace.com/gascp to play puzzles and word games.

Tell how the words seed and life cycle go together.

_____

_____

What Did You Learn?

 CRCT Prep

❶ (Circle) the correct answer.

❷ The stage that comes after the seed in

a plant's life cycle is _____.

❸ A new plant might _____ its parents.

❹ The stages of a plant's life cycle are

_____

_____

_____

142

Think About What You Have Read

 CRCT Prep

❶ A plant part where fruit and seeds form is a
   A. flower.
   B. stem.
   C. leaf.   S2L1c

❷ What stage comes after the seed in a plant's life cycle?

❸ How is a new plant like its parent plant?

❹ Describe the stages of a plant's life cycle.

Animal Life Cycles

What Do You Know?

List animals you know.
How do animals change as they grow?

_____

_____

_____

_____

_____

_____

Contents

What Do You Want to Know?

What do you wonder about how animals change as they grow?

_____

_____

_____

_____

_____

_____

_____

_____

_____

VOCABULARY

adult An animal that is full grown. *(noun)*

offspring The living things that come from a living thing. *(noun)*

reproduce When living things make more living things of the same kind. *(verb)*

VOCABULARY ACTIVITY

Break It Apart

offspring

Find the two smaller words in this word. Then say the words together. Write the two smaller words in this big word.

_____ + _____

 S2L1a. Determine the sequence of the life cycle of common animals in your area: a mammal such as a cat or dog or classroom pet, a bird such as a chicken, an amphibian such as a frog, and an insect such as a butterfly.

1 Which Baby Animals Look Like Their Parents?

All living things grow, change, and reproduce.

To **reproduce** is to make more living things of the same kind.

Babies are called offspring.

Offspring are the living things that come from a living thing.

Baby rabbits look like their parents.

Some offspring look like
their parents.
Some will grow to look like them.
Baby animals will become full grown.
An animal that is full grown is
an **adult**.

adult and baby
penguins

1. Living things come from _____

_____.

2. List three ways the baby penguin
looks like its parent.

_____

_____

_____

Circle the correct answer.

3. **Who do baby birds look like?**

Ⓐ eggs

Ⓑ baby mice

Ⓒ their parents

S2L1a

147

Summary   Animals grow and change during their life cycle. Many animals of the same kind look like their parents. What baby animals do you know that look like their parents?

_____

_____

▶ **Compare and Contrast**   How are parents and offspring alike and different?

Compare	Contrast
Parents and their offspring are the same kind of animal.	

Familiar Life Cycles

An animal changes as it grows. All of the changes are its life cycle. The stages in a life cycle are different for different animals.

A bird comes from an egg. It grows to be an adult bird.

Compare and Contrast

How are parents and offspring alike and different?

Which Baby Animals Look Unlike Their Parents?

Some young animals do not look like their parents.
They will grow to look like them.
Baby frogs do not look like their parents.
They will look like them as adults.

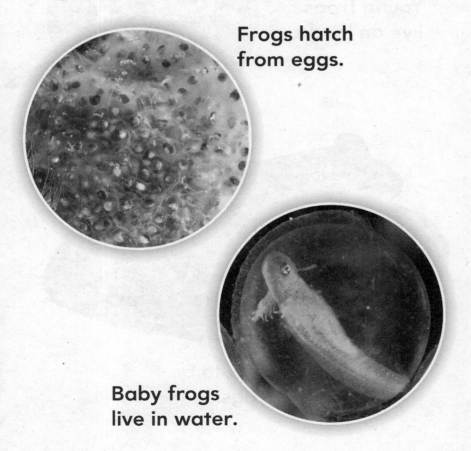

Frogs hatch from eggs.

Baby frogs live in water.

VOCABULARY

larva The worm-like stage in an insect's life cycle. *(noun)*

pupa The stage when an insect changes form. *(noun)*

VOCABULARY ACTIVITY

Use Syllables

larva

Break the word into syllables.
Say each syllable aloud.
Clap once for each syllable.
How many syllables does **larva** have?

_____

 S2L1a. Determine the sequence of the life cycle of common animals in your area: a mammal such as a cat or dog or classroom pet, a bird such as a chicken, an amphibian such as a frog, and an insect such as a butterfly.

1. Number the correct order of the life cycle of a frog.

_____ _____

2. Compare an adult frog to a young frog.

_____

_____

_____

Baby frogs are called tadpoles.
They come from eggs.
Tadpoles live in water.
They grow to be adult frogs.
Then they live on land.

Young frogs live on land.

They grow to be adult frogs.

Butterfly Life Cycle

A butterfly is an insect.

A baby insect does not look like its parent.

It starts as an egg.

A larva comes from the egg.

A **larva** is the worm-like stage in an insect's life cycle.

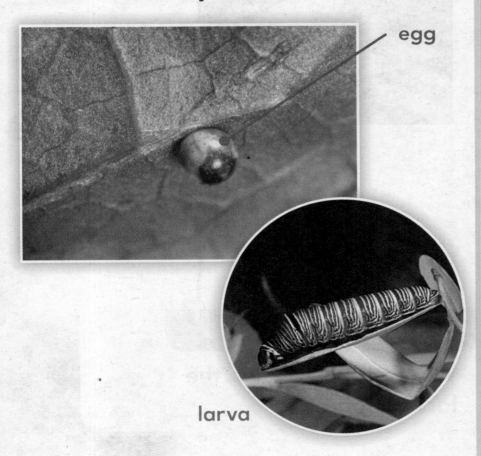

egg

larva

3. Circle the egg.

4. Put an X over the larva.

I Wonder . . . Larva is one stage in this animal's life cycle.
What will this animal look like when it is an adult? Draw a picture.

Summary

Some young animals do not look like their parents.

List young animals that do not look like their parents.

_____

_____

▶ **Sequence**   What stage follows the larva stage?

larva

↓

The larva grows into a pupa.
A **pupa** is the stage when an insect changes.
Then it looks like its parent.
The pupa grows into an adult insect.

pupa

butterfly

Sequence

What stage follows the larva stage?

Where Do Animals Get Their Traits?

Living things reproduce.
That means they make more living things of the same kind.
Plants and animals are living things.
They inherit traits from their parents.

Kittens are baby cats.

VOCABULARY

learned Traits that are not passed on from parents to their offspring. (*adjective*)

VOCABULARY ACTIVITY

Use Words

learned

The dog **learned** how to get the ball. Use clues from the sentence above to help you understand what the word **learned** means.

 S2L1a. Determine the sequence of the life cycle of common animals in your area: a mammal such as a cat or dog or classroom pet, a bird such as a chicken, an amphibian such as a frog, and an insect such as a butterfly.

Circle two of the children from this picture.
List two ways that they are different.

a. _____

_____

b. _____

_____

I Wonder . . . Why do cousins sometimes look like each other?

_____

_____

_____

When people reproduce, they have children.
Children of the same parents look like each other.
They are from the same family, but they are all different.
They may have different eye color.
The shape of their noses may be different.

These children look like their parents.

154

Learned Traits

Some traits are learned.
Learned traits do not come from parents.
You were not born knowing how to read.
Reading is learned.
Animals learn things, too.

This skunk learned where to find food.

Draw Conclusions

Why might kittens be the same color as their mother?

Summary   Some traits are learned instead of inherited.

What are some traits that you have learned?

_____

_____

▶ **Draw Conclusions**   Why might kittens be the same color as their mother?

> The mother and her kittens
> are the same color.

155

VOCABULARY

individual One living thing in a group of the same kind of living things. *(noun)*

VOCABULARY ACTIVITY

Use Pictures

individual

Say the word aloud.
Use clues from the picture to help you understand what the word means.

S2L1a. Determine the sequence of the life cycle of common animals in your area: a mammal such as a cat or dog or classroom pet, a bird such as a chicken, an amphibian such as a frog, and an insect such as a butterfly.

156

4 How Do Animals of the Same Kind Differ?

Animals in a family look like their parents.
They look like each other.
But they are not the same.
Each animal inherits different traits.
They may be different colors.
They may be different sizes.

These puppies are different colors.

An **individual** is one living thing in a group.
This family of dogs is a group.
Each dog is an individual.

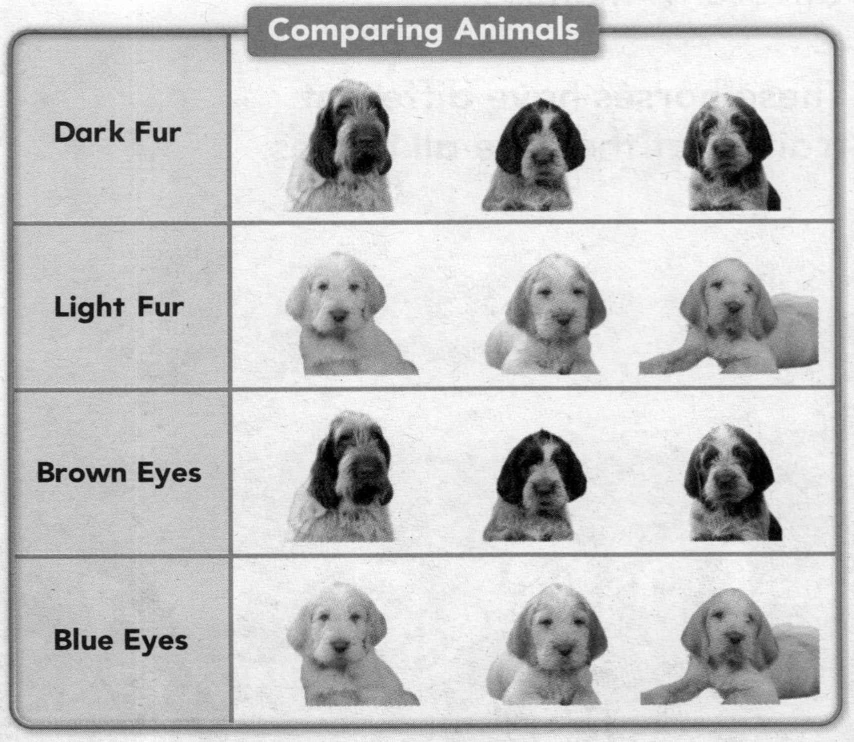

Comparing Animals	
Dark Fur	
Light Fur	
Brown Eyes	
Blue Eyes	

1. How are the individual dogs in this family different?

_____

_____

_____

_____

GPS **CRCT Prep**

Circle the correct answer.

2. What is a young dog called?

Ⓐ puppy

Ⓑ kitten

Ⓒ larva

S2L1a

157

3. (Circle) the horse population.

4. Put an X over an individual horse.

I Wonder . . . These horses are a population. Think of another animal population. Draw a picture of it.
Put an X on one individual in the population.

Animals in a Population Differ

A population is a group of the same kind of living thing in one place.
Animals in a population look like each other, but they are not the same.
Each animal in a population inherits different traits.

These horses have different traits, but they are all horses.

Animals look different because of the things around them, too. One may not eat much food. One may eat too much food. A sick animal may not grow very big.

These horses are from the same population, but they look different.

Main Idea

How can animals from the same population differ?

Summary Animals in a population inherit traits from their parents. What traits might an animal inherit from its parents?

_____

_____

▶ **Main Idea** How can animals from the same population differ?

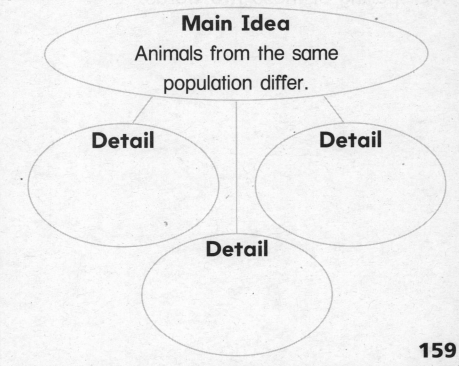

Main Idea
Animals from the same population differ.

Detail

Detail

Detail

Pick two science words. Write each word three times.

_____   _____

_____   _____

_____   _____

Work with a partner. Test each other on the spelling of these two words.

adult An animal that is full grown.

adult

individual One living thing in a group of the same kind of living things.

larva The worm-like stage in an insect's life cycle.

Glossary

learned Traits that are not passed on from parents to their offspring.

offspring

offspring The living things that come from a living thing.

pupa The stage when an insect changes form.

reproduce When living things make more living things of the same kind.

Visit **www.eduplace.com/gascp** to play puzzles and word games.

A butterfly starts as an egg.

(Circle) the three other stages of a butterfly life cycle.

Draw a picture of one of the stages.

What Did You Learn?

CRCT Prep

❶ Circle the correct answer.

❷ A dog might get its traits from

_____.

❸ An animal of the same kind might have

different _____.

❹ A trait that I inherited from my parents

is _____.

A trait that I learned is _____

_____.

Think About What You Have Read

CRCT Prep

❶ What are baby frogs called?
   A. pupa
   B. larva
   C. tadpole   S2L1a

❷ Where might a dog get its traits?

❸ How can animals of the same kind be different?

❹ What is a trait that you inherited? What is a trait that you learned?

PHOTOGRAPHY CREDITS